Bird Love

COLORING BOOK

DOT BARLOWE
RUTH SOFFER

COLOR
DOODLE
IMAGINE
CREATE

DOVER PUBLICATIONS, INC.
MINEOLA, NEW YORK

Whether scooting along the shoreline, nesting in trees, or soaring majestically through the air, nothing can match the unique beauty of birds. With more than 125 illustrations—from the Least Sandpiper to the Great Blue Heron, from the Common Loon to the Magnificent Frigatebird—this book will provide you with hours of coloring enjoyment. The name of each bird is provided on the page, so consult a bird guide to ensure accurate coloring and to learn even more about your favorite winged creatures. Unbacked plates allow you to experiment with different media, and the perforated pages make displaying your finished work easy.

Bibliographical Note
Bird Love Coloring Book, first published by Dover Publications, Inc., in 2016, is a new compilation of the following previously published Dover books: *Birds in Flight Coloring Book* (2013) by Ruth Soffer (plates 1–28); *The Birdwatcher's Coloring Book* (2012) by Dot Barlowe (plates 29–58); *Beautiful Birds Coloring Book* (2015) by Dot Barlowe (plates 59–89); *Exotic Birds Coloring Book* (2015) by Ruth Soffer (plates 90–120); and *Sea and Shore Birds Coloring Book* (1999) by Ruth Soffer (plates 121-127).

International Standard Book Number
ISBN-13: 978-0-486-81142-0
ISBN-10: 0-486-81142-5

Manufactured in the United States
81142501   2016
www.doverpublications.com

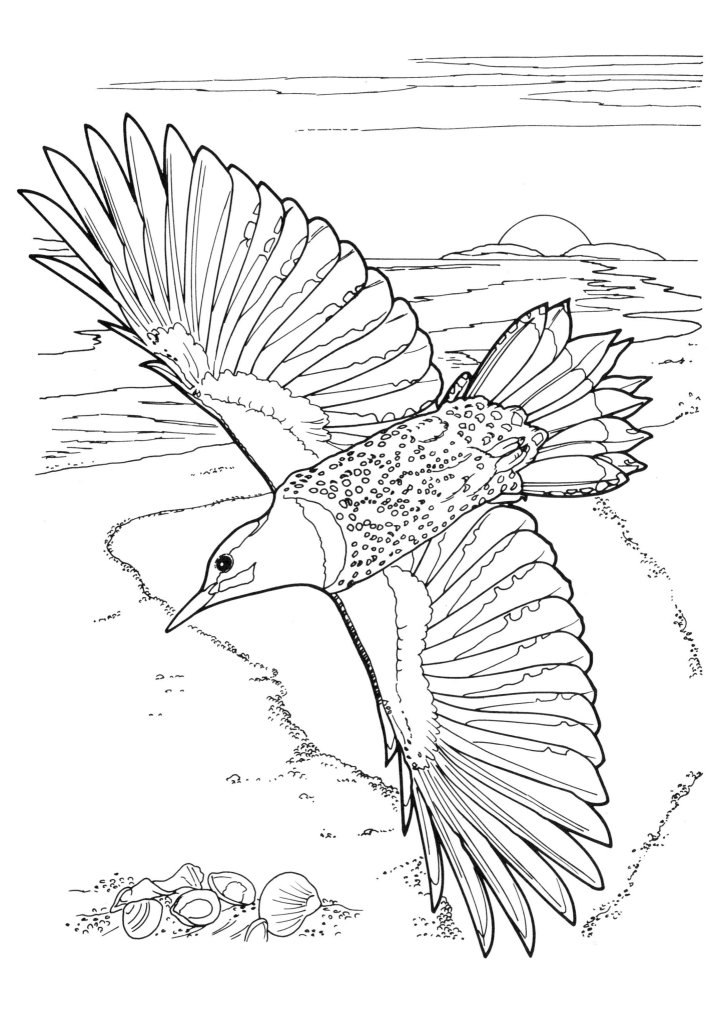

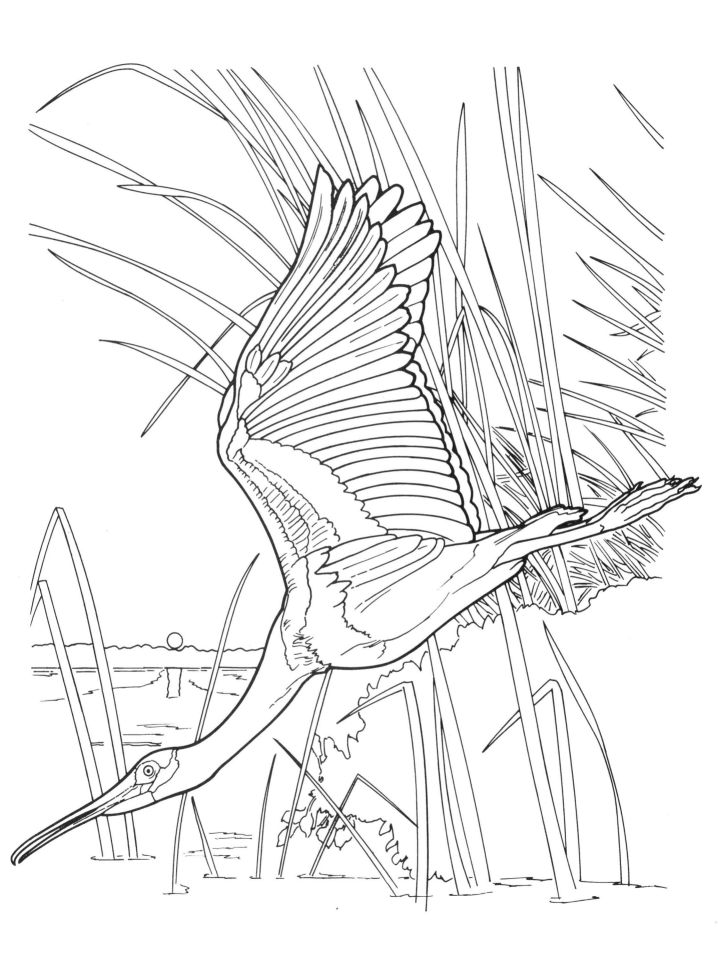

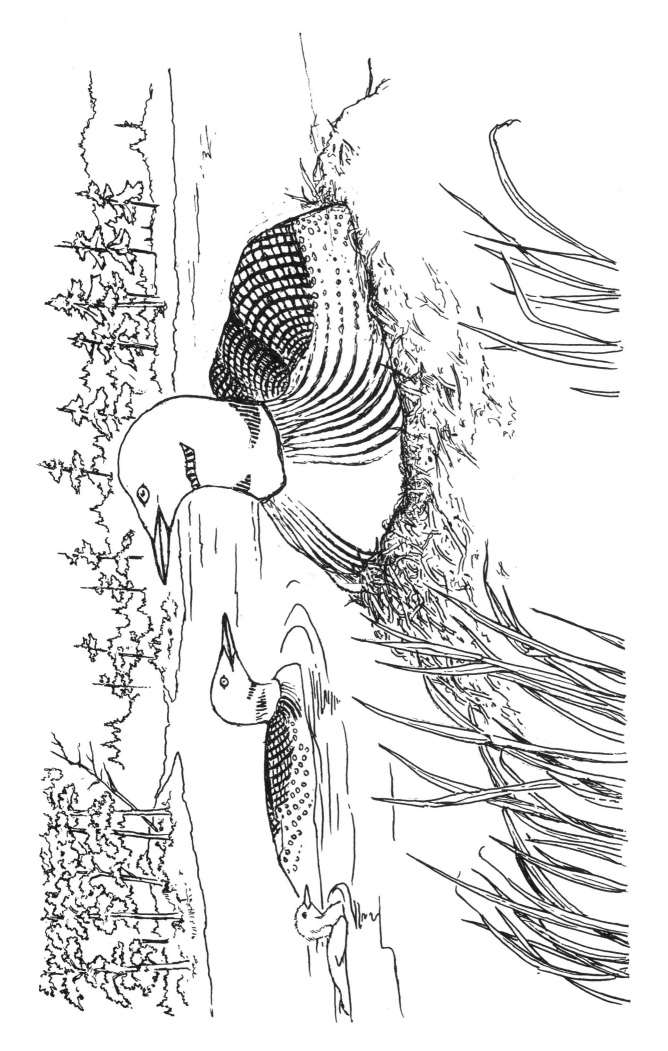

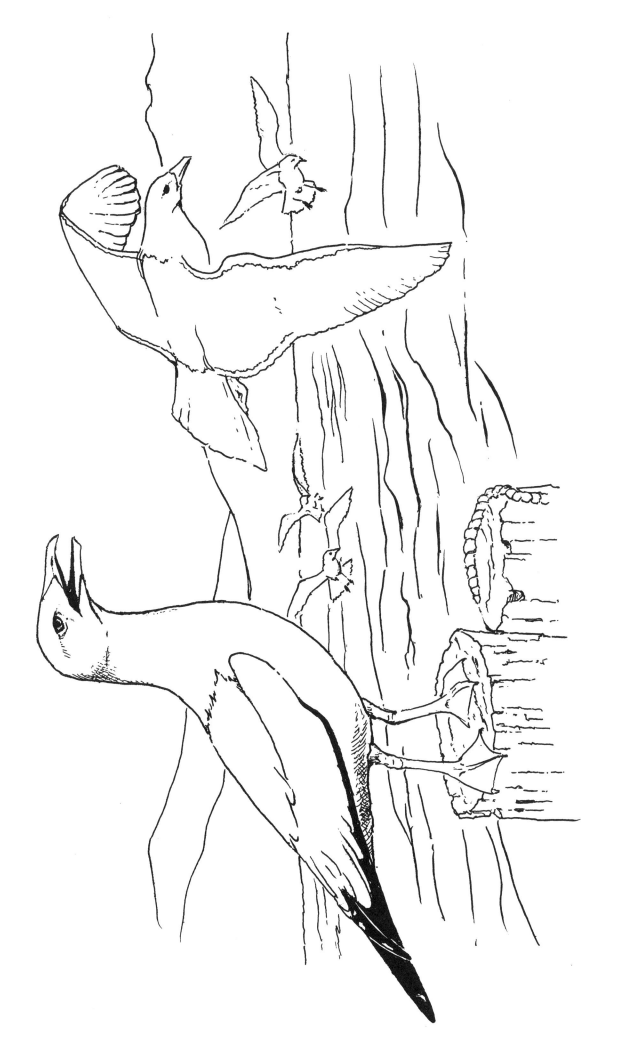

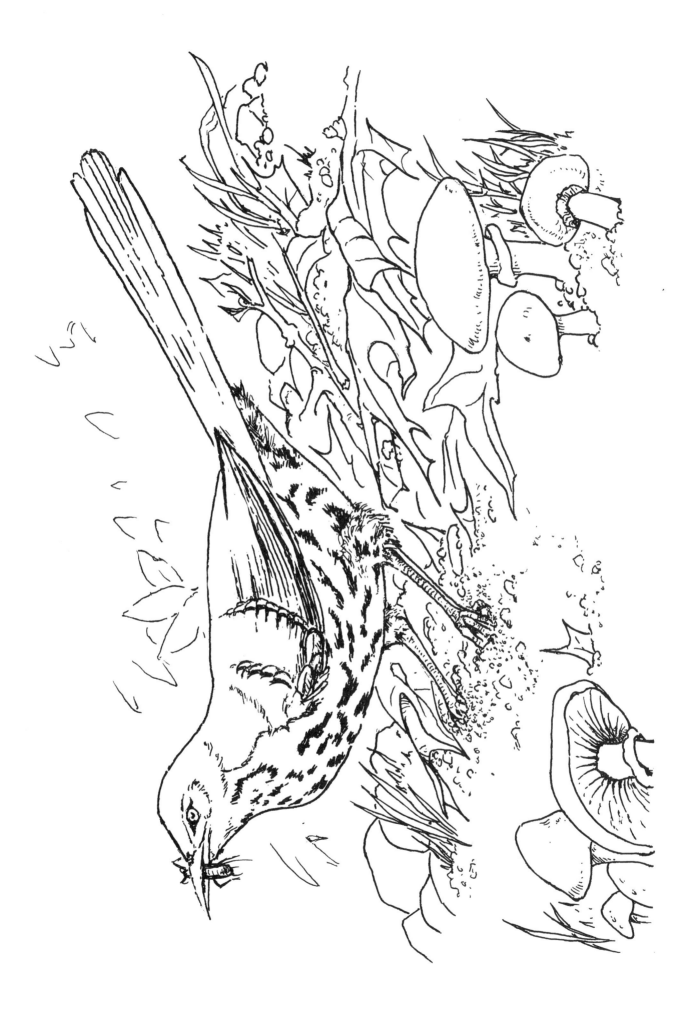

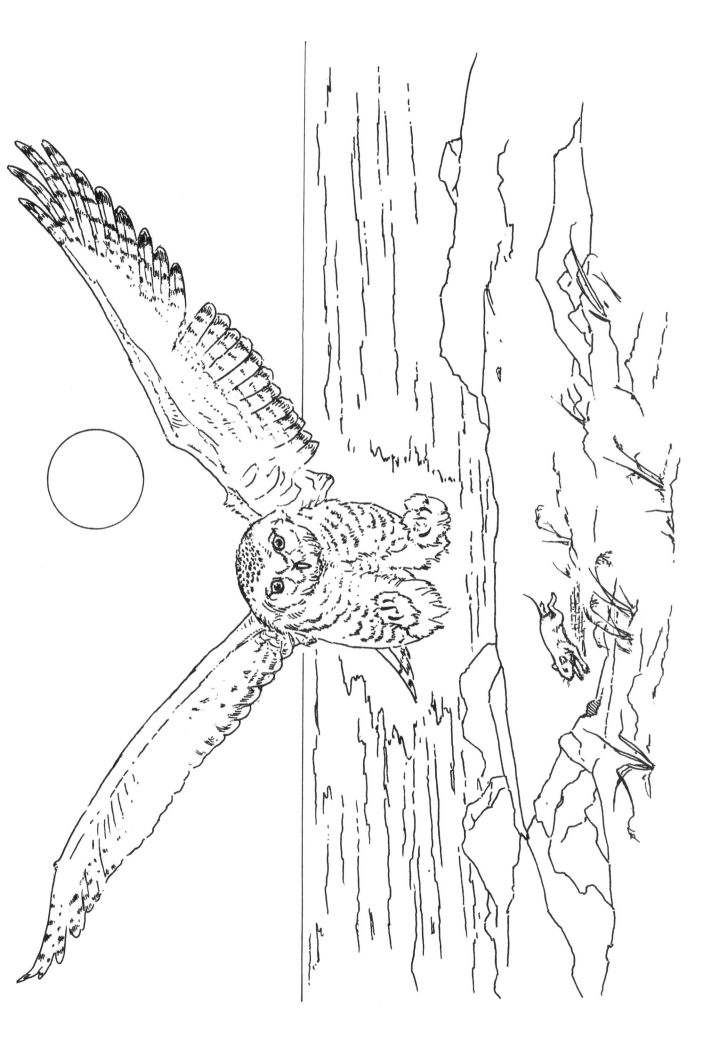

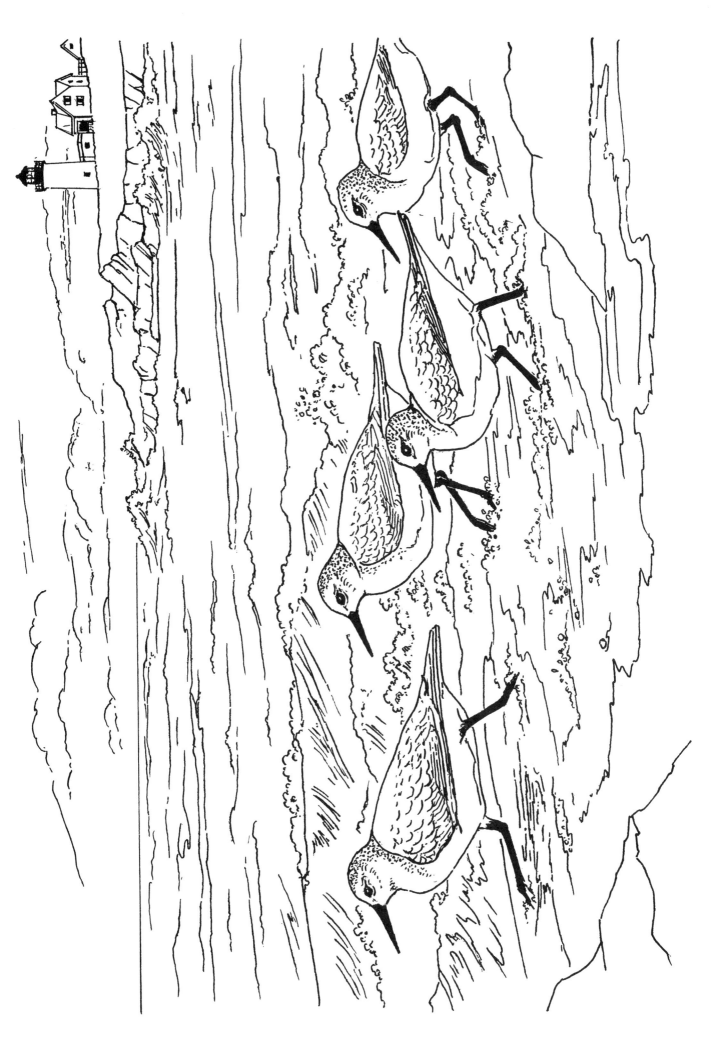

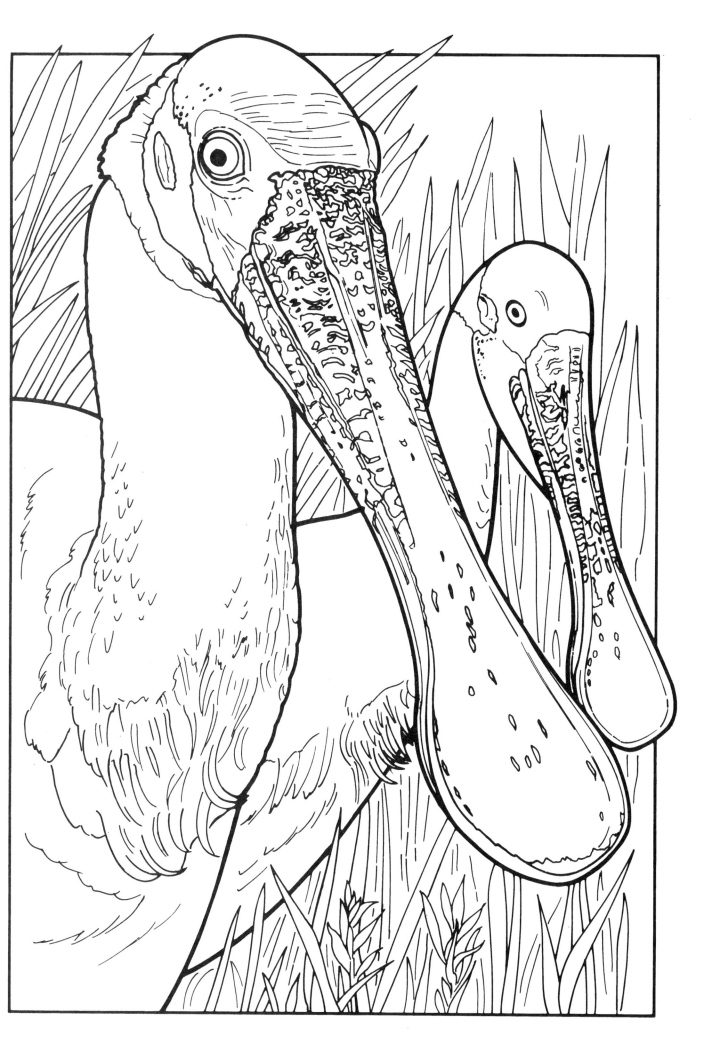